BIG BAD BRAD
THE HUMMINGBIRD

The Best!

Duane Ziegler

STORY BY DUANE ZIEGLER
ILLUSTRATIONS BY KATIE LAFRAMBOISE

BIG BAD BRAD THE HUMMINGBIRD
Written by Duane Ziegler

Illustrations by Katie LaFramboise

Edited by Kayla Henley

ISBN: 978-1-7337282-9-4

Library of Congress Control Number: 2021916359

Copyright © 2021 Duane Ziegler

Published by Duane Ziegler
Eagle, Colorado

Light of the Moon, Inc. - Publishing Division
Book Design/Production/Consulting
Carbondale, Colorado
www.lightofthemooninc.com

This book is dedicated to
the Eagle Valley Elementary School
Gypsum, Colorado

INTRODUCTION

Hmmm, hmmm, buzz, buzz, was the continuous sound from the little bird. With wings beating sixty times per second, Big Bad Brad the Hummingbird clipped along in the sky. Brad was on a mission: he had wintered in the pinewoods of Mexico and was headed to the Rocky Mountains of Colorado. He had rested up and was eager for adventure. As he flew, Brad did forward and reverse somersaults, full body rolls, and acted as if he owned the entire sky. If any bird entered his air space, he would let them know!

Just then, two blackbirds dared to fly below Brad.

Brad hollered, "Watch it, guys!"

George, one of the birds, squawked, "Hey, Tiny, who do you think you are? You trying to mess with Andy and me?"

Brad immediately dive-bombed the blackbirds, clipping their tail feathers. The blackbirds, of course, changed their flight plans.

Brad shouted, "This space is mine, mine, mine!" and laughed loudly.

Then Brad spotted a few female hummingbirds and joined them. Brad was always es-

pecially friendly to female hummingbirds. His goal this year was to have three female friends visit him at his Rocky Mountain home. Brad hoped to be settled into his home in ten days.

Day One

With whirling wings, diving and swooping, here came Big Bad Brad the Hummingbird. He dropped down into a mountain valley and then into a small town and focused on a tall blue spruce tree. He circled the tree, the house, and deck areas, and then landed in his old nesting area in the tree. Brad was back in his Colorado home!

Brad was now five years old, weighing three and a half ounces with a wingspan of four inches. He also had a patch of bright reddish-orange on his throat. Over time, Brad's name had changed from "Brad" to "Big Brad" as he got older. Now since he had to protect his home, he had changed his name to "Big Bad Brad the Hummingbird!"

Brad flew down to a lower branch of the tree to view his home territory. Below on

the west deck were many flowerpots and a hummingbird feeder. Directly below him on the south part of the deck, Brad noted more flowerpots, and on the east deck were even more flowerpots and another hummingbird feeder. Brad smiled to himself and thought, I flew from Mexico to be here at my home! Mine, mine, mine!

Day Two

Always alert, Brad spotted another hummingbird flying over the deck one day. The intruder drank from a feeder but then zipped away when Brad buzzed him and nipped him on his back.

Brad cried out, "I am Brad. This is my home! Stay away!"

The new hummingbird dipped and rolled, dove, circled the tree, and came around to the other feeder. He shouted, "My name is Rod, and I don't care who you are!"

Brad buzzed Rod, chased him around the tree twice, then around the house twice, until Rod gave up and flew off the property.

Brad circled back, drank from eight flowers and both feeders, and then flew up to a high tree branch in a nearby pine tree to watch his territory.

Still a little angry, Brad spotted a new visitor, but immediately recognized the green color. The visitor was a female hummingbird.

Brad flew down and greeted her. "I'm Brad. Welcome to my home. What's your name?"

"Hi, my name is Patty," the female hummingbird answered.

Brad showed her all the flowerpots and explained the differences between each flower. Finally, Patty rested on a tree branch. Brad sang some songs and showed off his flying trick moves for her.

Patty replied, "Yes, I am happy to be your friend, and I will build a nest in the blue spruce tree."

Day Three

The next day, two other hummingbirds silently arrived. Slim Tim stopped at one feeder and hollered, "Wade, the west feeder is open! Hurry up!"

Just then Brad yelled, "Boys, get lost! This is my home! I am Big Bad Brad the Hummingbird!" He zipped down, going one direction and then another. Brad chased one, then the other unwelcome guest.

Slim Tim and Wade were brothers and tried to use their diving and chasing tricks with Brad; one brother drank nectar while Brad was distracted chasing the other one. The longer the chase, the angrier Brad became. Brad whipped his wings harder and faster and eventually zapped Wade hard on the back and clipped Slim Tim on his tail. It took quite a while, but he finally chased them away. Brad stopped at the feeders to get some energy back.

Getting very little rest, Brad saw two more visitors had arrived. They were female hummingbirds. Brad asked for their names; his new guests were Jackie and Kasie. After

Brad welcomed them with a tour of the flowers, he sang songs, demonstrated his flying tricks, and danced in the air. Brad was very happy when they both agreed to build nests in the blue spruce tree. To celebrate, Brad visited both hummingbird feeders and drank from all the flowers in the flowerpots.

Day Four

During the night, the rain poured, and the branches of the blue spruce tree shook tremendously. About forty sparrows, four doves, and two finches had found shelter in the blue spruce tree, so in the morning there was a huge explosion of wings when Brad flew out of the tree. Brad checked on his guests and was very upset that two hummingbird nests had been destroyed. Also, because of the rain, the flowers below were wilted. Thus, there was a mad rush for the feeders since they were the only source of food.

Alert! Alert! Brad called out a warning to everybody. The people who lived in the

house had stepped out and were filling the hummingbird feeders. Brad noticed the people had also filled the bird feeders along the fence line and under the spruce tree. Brad knew the people weren't bad, but it also meant more birds would come to get the birdseed.

Brad said to himself, "Now there is a better chance that cats will come and try to catch a bird under the blue spruce tree! What should I do? What should I do?"

The people came out again and sat in chairs at the table. Brad decided he better buzz the people to make them leave. He circled and dove at the top of the man's head. Brad had to buzz three times before the man put up his arm and swatted at Brad. The woman had a newspaper and tried to keep Brad from buzzing her, but after two more buzzes, the woman got up and went into the house. Then Brad buzzed the man twice again; the man shouted at Brad and then went into the house after his wife.

Day Five

The next morning, Brad heard a commotion and hopped onto a lower branch to see what all the noise was about. He spotted two blackbirds on the table below; they were eating from a bag on the table. The people must have left crackers or something.

Brad shouted, "Both of you, time to get out of here! This is my place! I am Big Bad Brad the Hummingbird!"

The two blackbirds turned to look at him. The biggest one said, "Hey, we know you. You're that little bird nobody likes! I am George and my friend is Andy."

Andy joked, "You sure look funny!"

Hearing that, Brad dove so fast that he flew under Andy's legs, knocking him over. Then he spun and flew at George. George tried to whip his wings to rise in the air, but Brad was right on top of him, tapping hard into George's belly.

George fell backwards and roared, "Let's get out of here!"

As Brad watched the blackbirds fly away, he thought he had better check the feeders. He drank from all the flowers and both hummingbird feeders.

Day Six

Early the next morning, things were so quiet that Brad was still asleep, until an explosion of wings woke him. Birds were flying everywhere, getting out of the blue spruce tree.

Brad called out, "What's going on?"

Patty, one of Brad's friends, answered back, "Brad, I am on top of the wooden bear's head over here on the west deck. I see a cat crouched on the ground behind the blue spruce tree. I think he is trying to catch some sparrows feeding under the bird feeder."

Instantly, Brad flew down to battle the cat. Brad hovered in the air, about four feet above the cat, and announced, "I am Big Bad Brad the Hummingbird, and this is my home. Who are you and what do you want?"

The cat answered slyly, "I am Lionel. I saw all of the sparrows and I thought I could help them get to the birdseed."

"Yeah, and you would probably eat them too, you sneaky cat," Brad retorted.

Lionel suddenly swiped at Brad and missed. That made Brad even more upset. He buzzed Lionel and then rose high in the air.

Brad called for his hummingbird friends to join him. "My friends, let's show this cat that he is not welcome! Let's show him the way out of here!"

All of the hummingbirds dove at Lionel. The cat swatted at the birds but turned and ran off, howling from the stings they pecked on his back.

Brad thanked his friends and said, "Let's celebrate and drink nectar from the hummingbird feeders!"

Day Seven

The next night, Brad heard wings and a thud in the blue spruce tree. Then all was quiet until he heard, HOO, HOO, HOO! An owl had landed in the tree.

Brad didn't like that and shouted, "Why don't you go someplace else?"

The owl answered, "I am Nancy the Owl. I will hoot where and when I want. Should I come find you and eat you? I am an owl, don't you know?"

Unnerved, Brad stayed awake the rest of the night. In the morning, Nancy fixed her attention on the bird feeder under the spruce tree, looking for sparrows to hunt.

Brad sure didn't like the sight of that. He hovered in the air about fifteen feet above Nancy and declared, "I am Big Bad Brad the Hummingbird, and this is my home! I demand you leave!"

There was no answer from Nancy the Owl. Brad then called on his female hummingbird friends. Brad whispered an attack strategy to them, and after some discussion, all of them dove on Nancy, then circled back and dove again and again.

Nancy turned her head this way, that way, back and forth, up and down, around and around, but the birds kept attacking. Finally, Nancy shouted, "Enough, enough! I will leave!" and with that, Nancy rose into the air, whipped her wings, and quickly flew away.

Brad shouted, "Thank you, friends! Let's party and have fun at the feeders!"

Day Eight

The next morning, Brad was resting in the blue spruce tree when the quiet was broken by sounds of ratta-tat-tat, ratta-tat-tat.

Brad bounded out of his nest to see what was going on. Many small sparrows were rapidly flying away. Brad found a Red-Headed Woodpecker tapping very hard on the blue spruce tree upside down, which was upsetting the sparrows, along with Brad and his friends.

Brad flew around the tree, yelling at the woodpecker, "Who are you? You woke us up! This is our home!"

The woodpecker shouted back, "I am Alfred. Just wait a minute! You don't own this tree. I found this tree, so it is mine and you will have to move! I am hungry, so just leave me alone!"

Brad whipped his body so that he was upside down as well and flew all around the woodpecker. He sang songs, buzzed, and chirped at the woodpecker. He went on and on with the singing.

Alfred hopped around to the other side of the tree and teased, "Catch me if you can."

Brad, now really upset, flew right at Alfred again and again.

Alfred finally relented, "Enough! Enough!" and flew away.

Everything was again quiet at the home of Big Bad Brad the Hummingbird.

Day Nine

Brad was sitting on a wire that hung across the deck area, watching the sparrows on the ground under the bird feeder, when all of a sudden many of them flew away. A crow had silently landed under the tree.

Colton the Crow looked around and started stabbing at seeds on the ground. He walked with a swagger in his step, thinking, What a feast this is! The crow walked around and around, until he finally noticed Brad watching him. Colton cackled, "Who are you?"

Brad answered, "I am Big Bad Brad the Hummingbird! This is my home, and it is time you leave!"

Colton cackled again and said, "Are you going to make me? How silly are you?"

With that, Brad zipped down, circled around the tree, and came face-to-face with the crow. Brad dove under the crow's belly and legs and flew up behind Colton's back and pecked him on the back of his head.

"Ow! That hurts!" Colton cried, as he swiped his wing towards Brad.

Brad zipped under Colton and pecked one of his legs.

Colton staggered a bit and whipped his wings to restore his balance. Then he decided to just fly away, yelling to Brad as he left, "Have a bad day!"

Day Ten

The next day, Brad heard buzzing and flew down to see what was going on. As Brad

hovered just above and outside the west feeder, he saw six bumblebees swarming around it. Brad called out, "What is this? Who are you?"

The largest bumblebee answered back, "Hey, I am Samuel. We are as hungry as you are. Just look over at the other feeder: there are eight more bumblebees drinking there. Who are you anyway? Can't you share the feeders?"

Brad answered, "This is my home. I am Big Bad Brad the Hummingbird! I sure don't like that you just helped yourself to the feeders." But Big Bad Brad saw he was out numbered and zipped up to the overhead wire above the deck and plopped himself down. Well, he thought to himself, What should I do? I could get other hummingbirds to chase the bees. But since I have been so mean to everybody, they would not help me. What shall I do now? I sure don't want to starve!

Then Samuel asked, "Brad, have you bothered to be friends with the Red Ants and the Black Ants? They run up and down the iron rods that hold up the hummingbird feeders."

Big Bad Brad answered, "No, not at all."

"Well," Samuel said, "Don't be sad, Brad. It sure looks like you don't have any friends. You should travel around the valley for a day or two. Try to make some friends, smile a little. Come back here and be happy that you have a home. We have to fly everywhere to find our food. We don't have a home. You are so lucky! You should look for ways to make someone smile and offer some kindness."

Just then, Nancy the Owl glided down and landed on a tree branch. She said, "Brad, I came back to share with you some of my wisdom. One: creatures get mad when you treat them poorly. Two: life is short; spend it with friends who make you laugh and feel loved. Three: life is better with friends. Four: true friends can help each other. And five: For every second you are angry, you lose one second of happiness."

Big Bad Brad said earnestly, "Samuel and Nancy, your ideas make sense. I have been pretty nasty and hard on everyone." Then he called to the other hummingbirds. "Come, let's fly away and find as many flowers as possible and see if we can make some friends. I guess I should change my name back to just 'Brad'."

Samuel and Nancy nodded in approval.

Brad turned to Samuel and said, "Thank you! Thank you very much!" Then he turned to Nancy and said, "Thank you for helping me grow up."

The End

ABOUT THE ARTIST: KATIE LAFRAMBOISE

From an early age Katie has always enjoyed art and has been very creative. She has dabbled in all kinds of art from water colors, to acrylic paints, but her favorite is sketching, especially horses. She has a love for animals, so much so that she received a degree in Animal Science from Colorado State University in 2017. For the past couple years, she has enjoyed working as a Veterinary Technician and is very passionate about helping animals.

Illustrating children's books is recently a new endeavor. Katie loves helping the author's characters take form and come to life.

ABOUT THE AUTHOR: DUANE ZIEGLER

Award winning author, Duane Ziegler, was raised on a farm in North Dakota with five brothers. While he had a strong attraction to the wheat fields, pasture land, and rolling prairies, the mountains of Colorado have been the biggest influence in his life. He has been a professional educator for twenty years and a professional real estate agent for twenty-three years. He is a member of SCBWI, Colorado Authors League, and Roaring Fork Writers' Group. His immediate family includes his wife, Sandy, two children DeAnn and Nathan, four grandchildren, and one great-grandchild. He thanks the many people supporting him in creating children's fiction.

Visit Duane's Website
duaneziegler.com

Or connect with him on Facebook
@duanezieglerauthor

If you enjoyed this book, please visit duaneziegler.com
to learn about our other fun and educational books.

OTHER BOOKS BY DUANE ZIEGLER

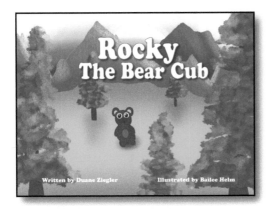

Rocky the Bear Cub follows a young bear cub named Rocky on his journey to say goodbye to all his forest friends before his first winter hibernation. Unfortunately, Rocky gets lost along the way while escaping a hungry coyote! It will take all his courage and the help of some new and unexpected friends to find his way back home in time for hibernation.

Goofus Galoofus is a young frog who dreams of being a cowboy and winning the Bullfrog Rodeo. Determined to prove his worth, Goofus disguises himself as a bullfrog and enters the Bullfrog Rodeo. But will his small size be able to match the other bullfrogs? And can he keep his true identity a secret?

Visit our website for new books, coloring books, and to meet the characters!

duaneziegler.com

CHECK OUT THE JIMJIM SERIES!

The First Book In The JimJim Series

JimJim and his mouse family live near Sylvan Lake, high in the Rocky Mountains. JimJim and his brother and sisters must overcome the dangers of rainstorms, being lost, escaping Mr. Owl, dodging Rusty the Hawk, and dealing with Mr. Black Bear. Throughout their adventures is the chance to achieve greatness as a mouse and claiming their second name. Follow JimJim and his three siblings on their journey to survive the wilderness with the help of their new friends.

The Second Book In The JimJim Series

JimJim and his mouse family live near Sylvan Lake, high in the Rocky Mountains. Trapped in a backpack, the mice find themselves in Las Vegas. They have exciting times, but get swept outside into the street by accident. The mice are attacked by alley cats, visit many places in Vegas, learn new dances, make new friends, and learn karate. Follow JimJim and JoeJoe as they survive Vegas and find a way to return to Sylvan Lake with the help of their new friends.

The Third Book In The JimJim Series

JimJim and his mouse family live near Sylvan Lake, high in the Rocky Mountains. After a harrowing trip to Las Vegas, JimJim and his brother JoeJoe have returned home with their new friends Dr. Bruce and his assistants Haley and Danielle. Together, JimJim, his siblings, and their friends travel around Sylvan Lake helping animals in need. Follow JimJim and company on their adventures as they help the animals of Sylvan Lake and make new friends like Toby the Turtle, Sleepy the Mouse, Noah the Bunny, and Happy the Fawn!

Visit our website for new books, coloring books, and to meet the characters!

duaneziegler.com

CHECK OUT THE SAMMY PUFFIN SERIES!

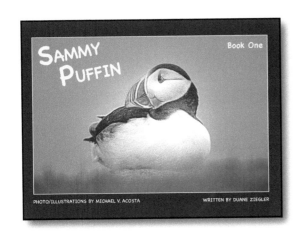

The First Book In The Sammy Puffin Series

Sammy Puffin and his puffin family live on the icy shores of Newfoundland where Sammy Puffin's parents teach him the ways of the puffin life: how to fly, catch fish, and spend time together. Follow Sammy as he has fun outings with Daddy Puffin and learns important lessons from Mommy Puffin.

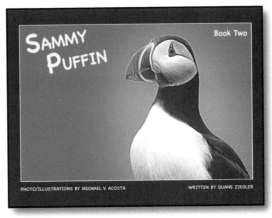

The Second Book In The Sammy Puffin Series

Sammy Puffin and his puffin family live on the icy shores of Newfoundland. Now that Sammy has learned the ways of puffin life, it is time to put his lessons to use as he and his family encounter dangerous predators like Red Fox and Black Mink. Follow Sammy as he grows from a baby puffin to a young adult ready to venture off on his own.

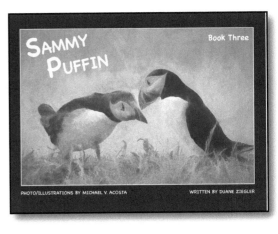

The Third Book In The Sammy Puffin Series

Sammy Puffin and his puffin family live on the icy shores of Newfoundland. Now that Sammy is grown, he must leave the island with the other adolescent puffins to explore on his own before returning to start his own family. Along the way he meets Sarah and they become parents. Follow Sammy and Sarah as they have their wings full raising two boys, who seem to find trouble wherever they go.

Visit our website for new books, coloring books, and to meet the characters!

duaneziegler.com

CPSIA information can be obtained
at www.ICGtesting.com
Printed in the USA
BVHW090450160422
634285BV00001B/6

* 9 7 8 1 7 3 3 7 2 8 2 9 4 *